学做中国菜
Learn to Cook Chinese Dishes

冷菜类 Cold Dishes

外 文 出 版 社
FOREIGN LANGUAGES PRESS

前　言

朱熙钧

倘若不是为想成为专业厨师，只是为了自家享用或偶尔飨客而学做中国菜，就无须专诚拜师学艺。中国主妇们的厨艺最初几乎都是从她们的老祖母和母亲那里耳濡目染学来的；待到为人妻母之后，她们之中的一些有心人再借助菜谱用心揣摩，或与友邻切磋交流，制作出的菜馔有时竟然不逊于出自名店名厨之手。当然，在中国的家庭中，擅长烹饪的男士也不在少数，而且饭店中的名厨以男性居多。

这套《学做中国菜》丛书的编撰者都是在名店主厨的烹饪大师。为了使初学者易于入门，他们以简明的文字介绍了每一菜式的用料、刀法、制作步骤等。读者只须按所列一一去做，无须多日便可熟能生巧，举一反三，厨艺大进。

《学做中国菜》系列丛书共九册，包括水产类、肉菜类、菜蔬类、豆品类、汤菜类、冷菜类、面点类、禽蛋类和家宴类。本册为冷菜类，介绍了 40 种家常食用的冷菜的烹饪方法。

冷菜又名凉菜、冷盘，是指经过加工、烹调、冷凉食用的菜肴。

冷菜不仅适合饮酒，也可佐餐，而且由于风味独特而自成一体，是一种方便食品，也是筵席上必不可少的菜肴。冷盘往往又是中国筵席上的第一道菜，具有第一印象的效应。

冷菜与热菜在烹调上是有区别的。大部分冷菜不需要上浆，也不勾芡；有些冷菜只调不烹。冷菜的特点是香嫩，无汁而又不腻。冷菜的香是越嚼越香，不同于热菜是随着热气散发的。因而冷菜的制作，要使用多种香料和调料，如花椒、八角、茴香、桔皮、丁香、葱姜、芝麻酱等，并配制成不同的调味卤汁。

冷菜由于风味、口感上不同于热菜，因而有十多种制作方法：有拌、腌、醉、糟、泡、盐水煮、白煮、卤、酱、冻、腊、风、熏等。

冷盘大多数是先烹调、后切配。冷盘讲究装盘，经过熟制的冷菜已酥软，切坏了不易返工，因而切配冷菜首先讲究刀工技法。根据熟料的不同性质，刀工上的轻、重、缓、急要恰当，切成的厚薄、粗细、长短要一致。

冷盘还讲究配色和造型。简单的家宴如用油爆虾、拌黄瓜、陈皮牛肉、白斩鸡四只冷盘，即由红、绿、黑、白对比的颜色进行组合，艳丽的色彩能刺激食欲。装盘还讲究色和形的和谐。两种以上菜肴进行拼盘，要注意到不同菜肴口味之间的配合，彼此间不要串味。菜肴和盛器之间的颜色也要协调。有时还可以用多种冷菜原料，拼摆成花鸟动物等形象或多种图案，增加美观。

Foreword

Zhu Xijun

You don't have to take lessons from a professional teacher to learn the art of Chinese cooking if all you want to do is to entertain your friends or cook for your family. Almost without exception, Chinese women learn this skill by watching and working together with their mothers or grandmothers. After they become wives or mothers themselves, the most diligent among them will try to improve their techniques by consulting cook books and exchanging experiences with their neighbors. In this way they eventually become as skilled as the best chefs in established restaurants. It should be noted, of course, that most of the well-known chefs in famous restaurants are men because many men in Chinese homes are just as good at the art of cooking as their wives.

This book in the *Learn to Cook Chinese Dishes* series have been compiled by master chefs. They have used simple explanations to introduce the ingredients, the ways of cutting, and the cooking procedures for each Chinese recipe. Readers who follow the directions will before long become skilled in the art of Chinese cooking. The entire set consists of nine volumes, covering freshwater and seafood dishes, meat dishes, vegetable dishes, courses made from soy beans, soups, cold dishes, pastries, dishes of eggs and poultry, and recipes for family feasts. This particular volume presents forty different cold dishes.

Cold dishes not only serve as appetizers, they are an important component of a whole dinner because of their unique flavors. In a typical Chinese feast, cold dishes are always the first to be served, thus having the function of giving the diner a first good impression.

The cooking skills for cold dishes vary a great deal from those for preparing warm dishes. Most cold dishes do not require any coating or thickening of the sauce with cornstarch. Some do not even need to be boiled or cooked, but can be made by simply mixing the required ingredients. Cold dishes are characterized by their aroma and tenderness. They do not contain sauce and are never greasy. Unlike many warm dishes that send forth their aroma into the air, cold dishes are usually sensed by taste rather than smell. Cold dishes, therefore, often make use of many kinds of spices and flavorings such as Chinese prickly ash, aniseed, fennel, orange peel, clove, scallions, ginger and sesame paste that are used to make sauces.

There are more than a dozen ways to make cold dishes, including mixing different ingredients, seasoning, marinating in wine, treating with distillers' grain, soaking with flavorings, boiling with and without salt, soaking in thick gravy, pickling with soy sauce, freezing, curing, drying, and smoking.

With cold dishes, the ingredients are processed or cooked before being cut and arranged on plates. Such dishes particularly emphasize the decorative factor when they are prepared. Since the processed ingredients are often quite soft and cannot be altered once cut, the technique of cutting is more important than it is for other types of Chinese cooking. The right strength, depth and speed of cutting must be employed according to the quality and nature of the ingredients.

Color and shape are two other important factors in preparing cold dishes. Simple family dinners can be provided with a four-course cold dish arrangement including previously quick stir-fried shrimps, cucumbers in sauce, beef with orange peel and boiled chicken. This combination offers a balanced fare and a contrast of red, green, black and white colors, which are likely to be very enticing. Harmony must be achieved in arranging the ingredients on a plate. One should pay close attention to the balance of different flavors in an arrangement of more than two kinds of cold dishes, allowing each dish to maintain its unique taste. Coordination between the ingredients and their containers must also be ensured. Often a number of ingredients are used to produce images of flowers and little animals or other beautiful patterns so as to increase the attraction of the dinner table.

目　录
Contents

名词解释 Terms Used in Chinese Cooking

上浆： 猪肉丝、猪肉片、牛肉丝、牛肉片、羊肉丝、羊肉片、鸡肉片在烹制前都要上浆。上浆大多用于滑溜、滑炒、清炒、酱爆等烹调方法。上浆好坏，直接影响烹调出菜肴的质量。上浆就是把切好的肉，用水冲洗净，放入盐、料酒、淀粉(有时也放鸡蛋)，拌匀后，向一个方向搅拌，感到有劲为止。

Coating (*shangjiang*): Shreds and slices of pork, beef, mutton and chicken have to be coated before they are cooked in such ways as slippery-frying, quick-frying and stir-frying. And how the meat is coated has a direct bearing on the quality of the cooked dish. The coating process involves first washing the cut meat, then adding in salt, cooking wine, and cornstarch(sometimes eggs are also used) and stiring well in the same direction until you feel it is a bit sticky.

刀工 Cutting techniques:

直刀法： 就是指刀同砧板垂直的刀法，分切、剁、砍，切是一般用于无骨的主料，剁是将无骨的主料制成茸的一种刀法，砍通常用于加工带骨的或硬的主料。

Straight-cutting: Holding the knife perpendicularly over the chopping board to cut, chop and heavy-cut the main ingredient. Cutting is applied to boneless meat ingredients, chopping is done to turn boneless ingredients into pulp or paste and heavy-cutting is used when preparing meat with bones or other hard ingredients.

平刀法： 是刀面与砧板平行的一种刀法，分推刀、拉刀。推刀就是把刀从刀尖一直推到刀根，拉刀就是把刀从刀根拉到刀尖。平切就是把刀一切到底。

Horizontal-cutting: Holding the knife flat against the chopping board to push it or pull it through the ingredients.Pushing means to push the knife through the ingredients from the knife's tip through to its end while pulling involves going through the ingredients from the end to the tip of the knife.

斜刀法： 刀面同砧板面成小于 90 度夹角的刀法。

Slashing: To cut by holding the knife in an angle smaller than 90 degrees from the surface of the chopping board.

花刀： 是在主料表面用横、竖两种刀法的不同变化，切(不断)出花纹，经加热后，主料卷曲成各种形状的刀法，有菊花形花刀，麦穗刀，鳞毛形花刀等。

Mixed cutting: To cut straight and then cross with sideways cuts to produce varied patterns. When heated, the ingredients cut in this way will roll up into different forms such as chrysanthemums, wheat ears and scales, according to the ways they are cut.

片： 用切或片的方法将原料加工成薄片。质地硬的原料用切，质地软的用片的方法加工成薄片。

Slicing (*pian*):By either cutting or slicing to turn the ingredients into thin slices. Hard ingredients require cutting while soft ingredients require slicing.

丝： 丝有粗细之分，一般在 0.2-0.4 厘米左右。一般先将主料切成 0.2-0.4 厘米的薄片，再将这些薄片排成瓦楞状，排叠要整齐，左手按稳主料，不可滑动，用刀把主料切成丝。

Shredding (*si*): The thickness of shreds usually varies between 0.2 (0±08 in) and 0.4 cm (0±16 in). First, either chunks of meat or vegetables are cut into thin slices of 0.2 to 0.4 cm in thickness. The slices are then arranged neatly like roof tiles.Pressed steadily underneath the left hand of the chef, the slices are finally cut into shreds.

条: 条的成形方法，是先把主料切成厚片，再将片切成条，条的粗细取决于片的厚薄。

Strapping (*tiao*):Main raw materials are cut into thick slices that are cut again into straps the size of which is decided by the thickness of the slices.

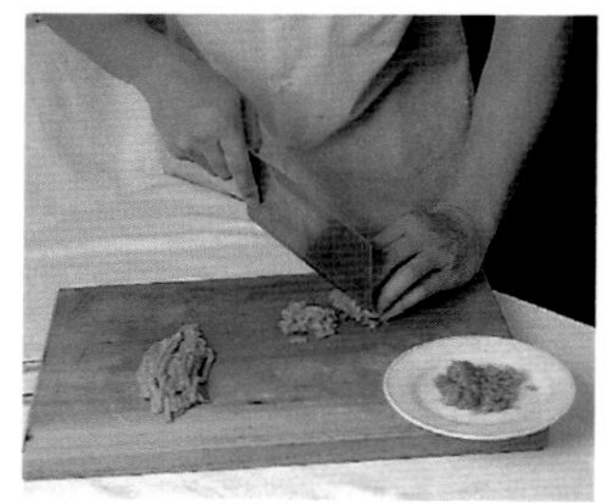

粒: 粒比丁小些一般在0.3厘米见方，切的方法同丁相同。

Grain-sized dicing (*li*): Cut in the same way as diced pieces, they are simply much smaller in size. The most common size is 0.3 cm (0.12 in) each side.

丁: 先将主料切成厚片，再将厚片切成条，然后再切成丁。丁有大小之分，大丁在2厘米见方，小丁在1厘米见方。

Dicing (*ding*): Main raw materials are cut into thick slices that are cut into straps. In turn, the straps are reduced to diced pieces that may be as large as 2 cm (0.8in) on each side or as small as 1 cm (0.39 in) on each side.

末: 末比粒还小，将丁或粒剁碎就可以了。

Mincing (*mo*): Ground ingredients are even smaller than grain-sized dices.Usually the diced pieces are chopped into mince.

茸: 用排剁的方法把主料剁得比末还细。

Chopping to make a pulp (*rong*): To chop the materials, knife cut after knife cut into pieces even finer than minced materials.

块: 块是采用切、砍、剁等刀法加工而成的。块分菱形块、方块、长方块、滚刀块等。

Cutting into chunks (*kuai*): Chunks are the result of perpendicular and sideways cutting as well as chopping. The chunks come in many shapes such as diamonds, squares and rectangles.

炸: 是旺火加热，以食油为传热介质烹调方法，特点是火旺用油量多。

Deep-frying (*zha*): Heat the cooking oil over a hot fire and deep-fry the materials. This process is characterized by a hot fire and a large amount of oil.

炒: 炒是将加工成丁、丝、条、球等小型主料投入油锅中，在旺火上急速翻炒成熟的一种烹调方法。炒分滑炒、熟炒、干炒等几种。滑炒是经过粗加工的小型主料先经上浆，再用少量油在旺火上急速翻炒，最后以湿淀粉勾芡的方法，叫滑炒。熟炒是把经过初步加工后的半成品，改切成片或块，不上浆，用旺火烧锅热油，放入半成品翻炒，再加佐料而成。煸炒和干炒是把主料煨一下，在热油锅急火炒至退水后，加佐料，起锅。

Stir-frying (*chao*): Put processed materials in the shape of diced pieces, shreds, straps, or balls into the heated oil and quickly stir them over a hot fire. There are several different ways of stir-frying. *Hua chao* (stir-frying with batter), for example, requires that the ingredients are put in a batter and then quickly stirred in a small quantity of oil over a hot fire.The final process is to apply the mixture of cornstarch and water. *Shu chao* (stir-frying precooked food) does not require that the materials be put into some kind of batter. Simply put the precooked materials into the wok and use a hot fire before adding spicing agents. *Bian chao* and *gan chao* (raw stir-frying) calls for the simmering of main ingredients, then quick-stir-frying over a hot fire until the juice is fully absorbed. Now add spicing agents and the dish is ready to serve.

溜：溜是先将主料用炸的方法加热成熟，然后把调制好的卤汁浇淋于主料上，或将主料投入卤汁中搅拌的一种烹调方法。
Slippery-frying(*liu*): First deep-fry the main ingredient and then top it with sauce or mix the main ingredient in the sauce.

爆：爆是将脆性主料投入适量的油锅中，用旺火高油温快速加热的一种烹调方法。
Quick-fry over high heat (*bao*): Put crispy materials into the wok with medium amount of oil and quickly stir the materials over high heat.

隔水炖：隔水加热使主料成熟的方法，叫做隔水炖。
Steaming in a container (*ge shui dun*): Put the main ingredient into a bowl or similar container and cook it in a steamer.

烧：烧是经过炸、煎、煸炒或水煮的主料，再用葱姜炝锅后，倒入翻炒，然后加适量汤水和调味品，用旺火烧开，中小火烧透入味 ，改用旺火使卤汁稠浓的一种烹调方法。
Stewing over medium,then high heat (*shao*): After putting scallions and ginger into the wok, put in the main materials that have been deep-fried, or stir-fried or boiled and stirred. Then add water and seasoning materials to cook over a hot fire until the ingredients boil. Turn the fire to medium or low to allow full absorption of the sauce into the ingredients before turning the fire hot again to thicken the sauce.

扒：扒是将经过初步熟处理的主料整齐地排放在锅内，加汤汁和调味品，用旺火烧开，小火烧透入味，出锅前，原汁勾芡的一种烹调方法。
Stewing and adding thickening (*pa*): Neatly arrange the main ingredient that has already been cooked,add water and flavoring materials and cook over a hot fire until it boils. Turn the fire to low to allow full absorption of the flavor. Thicken the sauce with the mixture of water and cornstarch before bringing the dish out of the wok to serve.

煮：煮是将主料放入多量的汤汁或水中，先用旺火煮沸，再用中小火烧熟的一种烹调方法。
Boiling (*zhu*): Put main materials of the dish into the wok with an adequate amount of water and cook it over a hot fire to the boiling point. Then continue to cook after turning the fire to low or medium.

烩：将加工成片、丝、条、丁等料的多种主料放在一起，炝锅翻炒后，用旺火制成半汤半菜的菜肴，这种烹调方法就是烩。
Precooking and then stewing (*hui*): First heat the oil in the wok, put in scallions and ginger and then put several kinds of main ingredients that have been cut into slices, shreds, chunks or dices to cook over a hot fire so as to create a dish of half soup and half vegetables and meat.

煎：煎是以少量油布遍锅底、用小火将主料煎熟使两面呈黄色的烹调方法。

Sauteing (*jian*): Put a small amount of oil into the wok and use a low fire to cook the main ingredient until it is golden brown on both sides.

蒸：蒸是以蒸汽的热力使经过调味的主料成熟或酥烂入味的烹调方法。

Steaming (*zheng*): Cook the materials that have already been prepared with flavoring agents by using hot steam.

拔丝：拔丝又叫拉丝，是将经过油炸的小型主料，挂上能拔出丝来的糖浆的一种烹调方法。

Crisp frying with syrup (*ba si*): Put small-size ingredients that have already been deep-fried into sugar syrup heated in the wok. When diners pick up the materials, long sugar threads are created.

焯水：就是把经过初加工的主料，放在水锅中加热至沸(主要为去腥味或异味)，原料出水后供烹调菜肴之用。焯水分冷水锅和热水锅。冷水锅就是主料与冷水同时下锅，水沸取出，适用于腥气重血量多的主料如牛肉、羊肉等。热水锅就是先将锅中水加热至沸，再将主料下锅，翻滚后再取出主料。适用于腥气小，血污少的主料如鸡、鸭、猪肉和蔬菜。

Quick boiling (*chao*): Put main ingredients into the pot and heat the water to boiling point(in order to remove fishy or other undesirable smells). Then cook the boiled ingredients. The quick-boiling process includes cold water boiling and hot water boiling. The former requires putting the ingredients into the pot toge ther with the cold water and then taking them out when the water boils. This process is often applied to such materials as beef and mutton,which contain a fishy smell and a lot of blood. The latter calls for heating the water in the pot to boiling point before putting the ingredients in.This is applicable to materials like chicken, duck, pork and vegetables that have a much weaker fishy smell and less blood.

油温表

油温类型	俗　称	油温特点
温油锅	四成 70℃－100℃	无青烟，无响声，油面平静。
热油锅	五、六成热 110℃－170℃	微有青烟，油四周向内翻动。
旺油锅	七、八成热 180℃－220℃	有青烟，油面仍较平静，用勺搅动有响声。

Temperatures of cooking oil:

Category	Temperature	Features
Luke-warm	70°C-100°C 158°F-212°F	Smokeless, soundless, calm oil surface
Hot oil	110°C-170°C 230°F-338°F	Slight smoke, oil stirs from the side to the center of the wok
Very hot oil	180°C-220°C 356°F-428°F	Smokes, the surface remains calm and when stirred, sizzling sound is heard.

花椒：花椒是花椒树的果实，以籽小，壳厚紫色为好。味香麻，烹调肉类的调料。

Prickly ash (*hua jiao*): Seeds from prickly ash trees, which are small and light purple in color. They have a slight effect of numbness on the tongue. Used to cook dishes with meat.

椒盐：味香麻，是炸菜蘸食的调味品。把花椒和盐按1:3的比例在锅中，微火炒成焦黄，磨成细末，即成。

Pepper salt (*jiao yan*): This mixture is made by stirring one portion of peppercorns and three portions of salt in the wok until they turn crispy yellowish in color and release their fragrance. Then finely grind the mixture into powder. It serves as a seasoning for deep-fried dishes.

味精：根据个人口味，也可不放味精，而使用适量的鸡精。
Monosodium glutamate and chicken bouillon: Though MSG is essential in traditional Chinese cooking, for many who do not find it agreeable, chicken bouillon can be used instead.

茴香：小茴香是茴香菜的籽，呈灰色，似稻粒，有浓郁的香味。
Fennel seeds (*hui xiang*): Seeds of fennel plants, grey in color and similar to unhusked rice grains in shape, have a hot flavor.

大茴香：又名八角、大料，形如星状，味甜浓，烹调肉类的调料。
Star anise (*da hui xiang*): In the shape of stars, they have a strong and sweet flavor. Mostly used in cooking meat dishes.

糟：制作料酒剩下的酒糟经过加工就成为烹调用的糟，糟具有同料酒同样的调味作用。
Steaming with distillers'grains sauce (*zao*): Distillers'grains, which are left over from liquor making, are processed into a spicy agent for cooking that has the same function as the cooking wine.

五香料：大料、茴香、桂皮、甘草、丁香(丁香花蕾)五种香料混合为五香料，研成粉为五香粉。

Five Spices (*wu xiang liao*): A mixture of powdered star anise, fennel seed, cinnamon bark, licorice root and clove buds. Also referred to as the "five-powdered spices".

桂皮：是桂树的皮，外皮粗糙呈现褐色。
Cinnamon (*gui pi*): The bark of cinnamon trees, brown in color.

料酒：常用料酒是用糯米等粮食酿制成的，料酒，在烹调菜肴过程中起去腥、增香的作用，特别是烹制水产或肉类时少不了它。如没有料酒，可用适量的啤酒或白兰地代替，但没有料酒好。
Cooking wine (*liao jiu*): Cooking wine, brewed from grain, is applied to remove the fishy smell and increase the aroma of the dish. It is particularly essential when cooking dishes with aquatic ingredients and meat. While cooking wine is most desirable, in its absence, beer and brandy can be used.

勾芡：勾芡就是在菜肴接近成熟时，将调好的湿淀粉加入锅内，搅拌均匀，使卤汁稠浓。增加卤汁对主料的附着力的一种方法。
Thickening with mixture of cornstarch and water (*gou qian*): When the dish is nearly cooked, put a previously prepared mixture

of cornstarch and water into the dish and stir well so as to thicken the sauce or broth. This process promotes the flavored sauce to stay with the main materials of the dish.

勾芡作用：1、增加菜肴汤汁的粘性和浓度。2、增加菜肴的光泽。

Major functions of this process: (1) Increase the stickiness and thickness of the sauce of the dish. (2) Making the dish look more shiny.

勾芡关键：1、勾芡必须在菜肴即将成熟时候进行。2、勾芡时锅中汤汁不可太多或太少。3、必须在菜肴的口味、颜色已经调准后进行。4、勾芡时锅中油不宜太多。

Key for using this process: (1) This process must be conducted when the cooking of the dish is nearly complete. (2) The sauce in the wok must not be too much or too little when this thickening technique is applied. (3) This process can only be done after all efforts for flavoring and coloring of the dish are completed. (4) When doing the thickening process, the wok should not have too much oil in it.

如何使用筷子

吃中式饭菜一般使用筷子。筷子是用木或竹、骨及其它材料制成长25-30厘米、上方（各边为8毫米）下圆（直径为3-5毫米）的二根小棍。

使用时须依靠拇指及食指、中指和无名指的连贯配合。方法是：首先把两根筷子拿在右手，用食指、中指及无名指在距筷子近上端处各夹一根筷子，再把拇指和食指合在一起，如图1。用筷子取食时，把食指和中指夹的一根向上抬，另一根不动，使两根筷子张开。如图2。夹取食物时，把食指和中指夹的筷子往下压，夹住食物，抬起筷子进食，如图3。

How to Use Chopsticks

Chopsticks for eating Chinese food are usually made from wood, bamboo, animal bones or other materials. About 25 to 30 centimeters long, their top is square, about 0.8 square centimeter, and the low end round with a diameter of 3 to 5 millimeters.

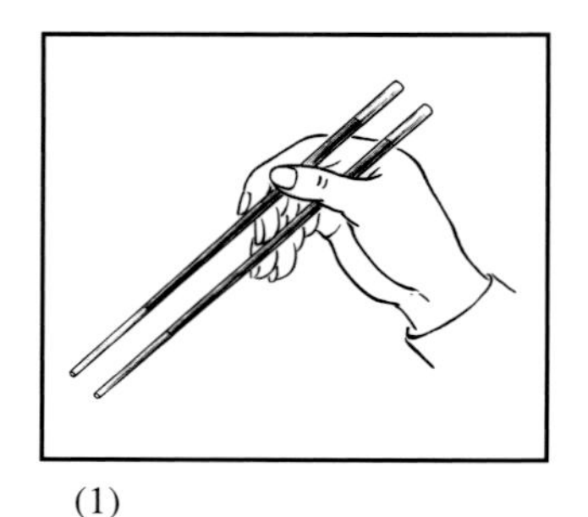

(1)

(2)

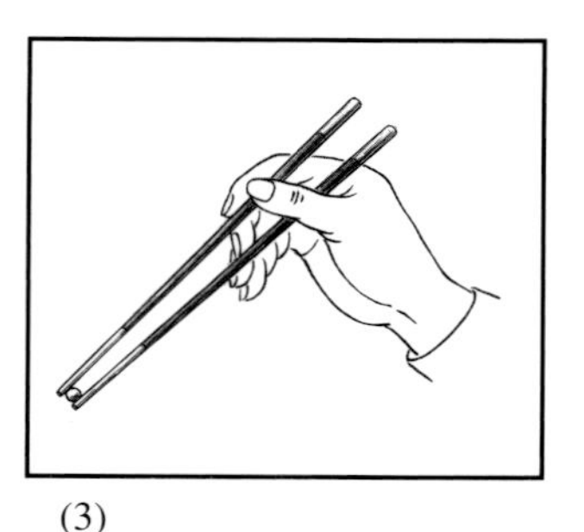

(3)

The correct way of using the chopsticks requires concerted efforts of the thumb, index finger, middle finger and third finger. Hold the pair of chopsticks in the right hand, using the index finger, middle and third fingers to keep the chopsticks steady near their top and then push them open by moving the thumb and index finger. (See Drawing 1)

To pick things up with chopsticks, lift upward one of the two chopsticks with the index and middle fingers while keeping the other one where it is so as to separate the two. (See Drawing 2)

Once the chopsticks have picked up the food, press one of the chopsticks with the thumb and index finger and raise the pair. (See Drawing 3)

笼屉　蒸锅
Steaming tray(***long ti***)Usually made of bamboo or wood, these often come in several tiers

炒锅
Skillet

火锅
Hot-pot

砂锅
Earthen pot

汤勺　炒铲　漏勺
Soup spoon　Shovel　Perforated spoon

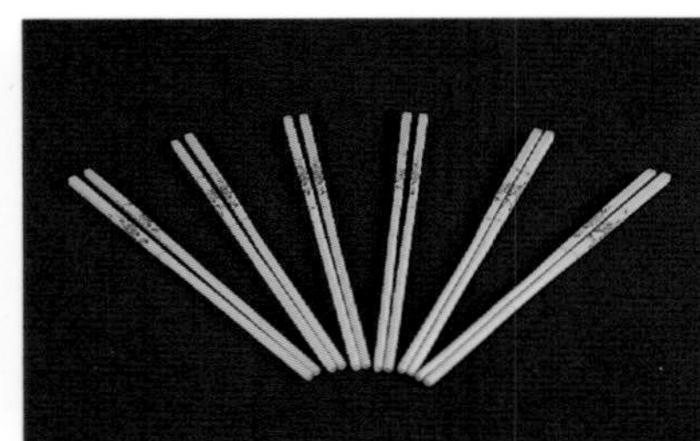

筷子
Chopsticks

菜（面）板
Chopping board

油爆大虾

主料：活大虾 500 克

调料：料酒 50 克、糖 25 克、盐 3 克、姜末 5 克、葱末 10 克、水 100 克、油 1000 克（实耗 75 克）

制作：①虾剪去须脚，抽去沙筋，洗净放入碗中，加盐 2.5 克、料酒 15 克拌匀，倒入漏勺待用。

②旺火热锅，加油待油温升到八成热时，将虾倒入油锅炸 2 分钟，再倒入漏勺。

③原锅留油 10 克，放入葱姜末煸炒 10 钞钟，倒入虾，加料酒、盐、糖、水烧沸，翻炒数次出锅即成。

特点：虾壳脆而易脱

口味：甜中带咸

Quick Stir-fried Prawns

Ingredients:

500 grams (1.1 lb) live prawns
50 grams (3 1/2 tbsp) cooking wine
25 grams (1 3/4 tbsp) sugar
3 grams (1/2 tsp) salt
5 grams (1/6 oz) chopped ginger
10 grams (1/3 oz) finely cut scallions
100 grams (6 tbsp) water
1000 grams (2 cups) oil (only 75 g or 5 1/2 tbsp to be consumed)

Directions:

1. Cut off the feelers and legs of the prawns and remove the tendon on their backs. Wash them clean and put them in a bowl. Add 2 1/2 g (under 1/2 tsp) salt, 15 g (1 tbsp) cooking wine and mix well. Put in a strainer for later use.

2. Heat the oil in a wok to 200-220 °C (390-430 °F) and deep-fry the marinated prawns for 2 minutes. Take them out and put them back into the strainer.

3. Keep 10 g (2 tsp) of oil in the wok and stir-fry the scallions and ginger for 10 seconds. Add the prawns, then the cooking wine, salt, sugar and water and bring to a boil. Turn over several times and take out. The dish is ready. Serve when it cools.

Features: The shells are crispy and easy to take off the prawns.

Taste: Sweet with a salty touch.

油爆大虾
Quick Stir-fried Prawns

拌三丝

主料：猪里脊肉125克、鸡脯125克、桂鱼肉125克

辅料：青椒一只、胡罗卜30克

调料：鸡蛋1只、料酒5克、盐3克、麻油15克、干淀粉10克、葱椒酒5克（葱和花椒泡在料酒中十分钟即成葱椒酒）、姜丝5克

制作：①将猪里脊肉及鸡脯肉去筋膜，同桂鱼肉一起，分别切成长约5厘米的细丝，用蛋清、料酒、盐1.5克、干淀粉上浆备用。青椒、胡罗卜洗净切细丝。

②分别将三丝在沸水锅中煮5分钟，青椒、胡罗卜丝在沸水中煮1分钟，并捞出沥干水分。

③三丝置盘中，加葱椒酒拌和，滤去卤汁，再加麻油、盐1.5克拌和即成。姜丝装碟随口味拌用。

特点：味清淡，鲜嫩爽口

口味：咸鲜

Combination of Shredded Meat

Ingredients:

125 grams (0.27 lb) pork tender loin
125 grams (0.27 lb) chicken breast
125 grams (0.27 lb) Mandarin fish
1 green pepper
30 grams (1 oz) carrot
1 egg
5 grams (1 tsp) cooking wine
3 grams (1/2 tsp) salt
15 grams (1 tbsp) sesame oil
10 grams (1 1/2 tbsp) dry cornstarch
5 grams (1 tsp) scallions and peppery wine (made by soaking a small number of scallions and Chinese prickly ash in cooking wine for 10 minutes)
5 grams (1/6 oz) sliced ginger

Directions:

1. Cut the three kinds of meat into thin shreds 5 cm (2 inches) long and marinate the shredded meat with the egg white, cooking wine, 1 1/2 g (1/4 tsp) salt and dry cornstarch. Wash clean and cut the green pepper and carrot into thin shreds.

2. Boil the shredded meat separately, each for 5 minutes. Boil the shredded green pepper and carrot for 1 minute. Take out and drain off the water.

3. Put the shredded meat on a plate, add the scallions and peppery wine and mix well. Get rid of the sauce that results from the mixing. Add the sesame oil and 1 1/2 g (1/4 tsp) salt and mix well. Put the shredded ginger in a small plate to go with the dish.

Features: Light-seasoned, the dish is refreshing and soothing to the mouth.

Taste: Salty and delicious.

拌三丝
Combination of Shredded Meat

水晶肴肉

主料：去爪猪蹄 1 只约 1500 克

调料：盐 150 克、料酒 25 克、葱段 15 克、姜片 15 克、桂皮 10 克、茴香 5 粒、花椒 10 粒

制作：①将猪蹄去毛、刮洗净，去骨。

②蹄皮朝下平摊在砧板上，用铁筷尖（可用类似器具代替）戳若干小孔，然后用盐擦抹带皮的一面，两面均抹上葱、姜、桂皮、茴香、花椒，放入深盘中加盖，夏季腌 2 天，春秋季腌 3 天，冬季腌 1 周。

③剔除葱、姜、香料，将猪蹄冲洗干净放入盘中。放清水 100 克，上笼用旺火蒸 2 小时取出，将猪蹄铺开放入另一个干净的盆中并将汤汁浇至同猪蹄平。待其冷却成冻后切成长约 5 厘米，宽 3 厘米，厚约 0.7 厘米的块装盘。

特点：晶莹透亮

口味：鲜香肉嫩

Crystal Pork

Ingredients:

1 pig's foot (about 1,200 g or 2.6 lb)
150 grams (1/3 lb) salt
25 grams (1 3/4 tbsp) cooking wine
15 grams (1/2 oz) sectioned scallions
15 grams (1/2 oz) sliced ginger
10 grams (1/3 oz) cinnamon
5 grains of fennel
10 grains of Chinese prickly ash

Directions:

1. Dress the pig's foot and remove the bone.

2. Put the foot on a chopping board with the skin side down. Prick several holes in it with an iron chopstick or other pointed utensil. Rub salt on the skin side, but put scallions, ginger, cinnamon, fennel and Chinese prickly ash on both sides. Put it in a deep container and cover the lid. Marinate for 2 days in summer, or alternatively 3 days in spring and fall and 1 week in winter.

3. Get rid of the scallions, ginger and other spices. Wash the pork foot clean and put on a plate. Add 100 g (6 tbsp) of water and steam over strong fire for 2 hours. Take out and put the pork foot in a bowl. Pour on the juice resulting from steaming until the meat and the sauce are at the same level. When it totally cools off and solidifies into a jelly form, cut foot into chunks 5 cm (2 inches) long, 3 cm (1.2 inches) wide and 0.7 cm (0.28 inch) thick. Place on a plate and serve.

Features: Crystal and transparent.
Taste: The meat is tender and refreshing.

水晶肴肉
Crystal Pork

陈皮牛肉

主料：牛肉 500 克

调料：葱段 5 克、姜片 3 克、料酒 25 克、酱油 10 克、盐 2 克、糖 5 克、陈皮 25 克（盐渍过的桔皮）、油 15 克

制作：①将牛肉切成长约 3 厘米、宽约 1.7 厘米、厚约 0.3 厘米的薄片，用料酒、酱油、盐、葱段、姜片、陈皮拌匀，放入冰箱中 1 小时。

②温火热锅，用油将锅抹一下，倒入肉片，用铁筷（可用家常用器具代替）不断翻拨牛肉直至水份烘干，肉片成熟略脆，香味透出（约 20 分钟），拣去陈皮、葱段、姜片，加糖拌匀出锅即成。

特点：色艳

口味：香脆

Beef with Dried Orange Peel

Ingredients:

500 grams (1.1 lb) tender beef
5 grams (1/6 oz) sectioned scallions
3 grams (1/10 oz) sliced ginger
25 grams (1 3/4 tbsp) cooking wine
10 grams (1 1/2 tsp) soy sauce
2 grams (1/3 tsp) salt
5 grams (1 tsp) sugar
25 grams (5/6 oz) dried orange peel
15 grams (1 tbsp) cooking oil

Directions:

1. Slice the beef to 3 cm (1.2 inches) long, 1.7 cm (0.6 inch) wide and 0.3 cm (0.12 inch) thick and mix with the cooking wine, soy sauce, salt, scallions, ginger and orange peel. Put in the refrigerator for 1 hour.

2. Heat the oil to 70-100 °C (160-210 °F), put in only the beef slices and keep stirring and turning until all the moisture is gone. This process takes about 20 minutes after which the beef slices become crispy and produce an attractive aroma. Now add the orange peel, scallions, ginger, sugar and mix well. Take out to serve.

Features: Brightly colored.
Taste: Crispy and aromatic.

陈皮牛肉
Beef with Dried Orange Peel

生菜鸡丝

主料：生鸡胸脯肉 250 克

辅料：生菜 20 克

调料：白酱油 10 克、糖 2 克、味精 1 克、鸡汤 25 克

制作：①生菜洗净，部分平铺在盘面上，部分切成丝。②将生鸡脯肉煮熟，冷却后撕成细丝。加入生菜丝、冷鸡汤 25 克、白酱油、糖、味精拌和后放在生菜上即成。

特点：色艳

口味：鲜嫩

Shredded Chicken with Lettuce

Ingredients:

250 grams (0.55 lb) chicken breast
20 grams (2/3 oz) lettuce
10 grams (1 1/2 tsp) light-colored soy sauce
2 grams (2/5 tsp) sugar
1 gram (1/4 tsp) MSG
25 grams (1 2/3 tbsp) chicken soup

Directions:

1. Wash the lettuce clean and spread some of the leaves flat on a plate. Shred the rest of it.

2. Boil the chicken breast until it is done. When it cools off, cut the chicken into thin shreds. Mix these with the lettuce shreds, cold chicken soup, light-colored soy sauce, sugar and MSG, and place the mixture on top of the lettuce leaves on the plate.

Features: Beautifully colored.
Taste: Tender and refreshing.

生菜鸡丝
Shredded Chicken with Lettuce

盐水牛肉

主料：牛肉 500 克

调料：葱结 5 克、姜块 3 克、料酒 20 克、盐 10 克

制作：①将牛肉洗净，放入锅中加水烧沸，取出牛肉洗净血沫，撇去汤中浮沫，加葱、姜、盐、料酒，加盖烧沸后，转文火煮 2 小时。

②将牛肉浸泡在原汤汁里，待其冷却后，切成长 6 厘米，宽 4 厘米，厚 0.3 厘米的薄片装盘，浇上少许原汤汁即成。

特点：酥烂入味

口味：咸中带鲜

Salted Beef Slices

Ingredients:

500 grams (1.1 lb) tender beef
5 grams (1/6 oz) sectioned scallions
3 grams (1/10 oz) ginger chunks
20 grams (1 2/3 tbsp) cooking wine
10 grams (1 2/3 tsp) salt

Directions:

1. Boil the beef and skim off the foam. Add the scallions, ginger, salt and cooking wine, and cover up the pot to again bring it to a boil. Turn to a low fire to simmer for 2 hours.

2. Continue to soak the beef in the juice until it cools off. Then cut the beef into slices 6 cm (2.4 inches) long, 4 cm (1.6 inches) wide and 0.3 (0.12 inch) thick. Place on a plate and pour on some of the juice.

Features: The meat is soft and richly flavored.
Taste: Salty and delicious.

盐水牛肉
Salted Beef Slices

糟鸭蛋

主料：鸭蛋 10 只

调料：香糟 100 克（超市有卖）、盐 30 克、葱 10 克、姜 10 克、花椒 3 克、料酒 500 克

制作：①锅内放水 500 克，加盐、葱、姜烧沸，冲入放有花椒的容器中，再将料酒、香糟拌入其中浸 20 分钟。

②将鸭蛋加冷水煮熟去壳，冷却后放入香糟卤内加盖置冰箱中，3—6 小时后取出切好装盘。

特点：黄白相间

口味：蛋鲜香

Duck Eggs in Wine Sauce

Ingredients:

10 duck eggs
100 grams (1/5 cup) distillers' grain (to be found in Chinese grocery stores)
30 grams (5 tsp) salt
10 grams (1/3 oz) scallions
10 grams (1/3 oz) ginger
3 grams (1/10 oz) Chinese prickly ash
500 grams (1 cup) cooking wine

Directions:

1. Put 500 g (1 cup) of water in a pot and add the salt, sectioned scallions and ginger chunks and bring to a boil. Put this in a container already containing the Chinese prickly ash. Add the cooking wine and distillers' grain and let it stand for 20 minutes.

2. Boil the eggs. Remove the shells when they are cool and put into the sauce, put the cover on the container and place in the refrigerator for 3 to 6 hours. Take out, cut into halves or quarters before serving.

Features: The dish has a nice combination of white and yellow colors.
Taste: Salty and delicious.

糟鸭蛋
Duck Eggs in Wine Sauce

盐水鸭

主料：活肥鸭一只约 2500 克

调料：料酒 150 克、盐 80 克、葱 20 克、姜块 5 克、大茴香 20 克、桂皮 20 克

制作：①将鸭退毛去内脏，洗净，用盐 50 克遍擦鸭身及腹腔内，放在盆内腌 5 小时左右，取出滤去盐水。

②鸭放入锅中加水烧沸，取出洗净，撇去汤中浮沫，鸭放回原汤锅。

③锅内放入葱、姜、大茴香、桂皮、盐，加盖用旺火煮沸后倒入料酒改用文火烧焖 40 分钟，至鸭八成烂熟时取出，待冷却后切块装盘，浇上原汤即可。

特点：色白肉嫩

口味：咸鲜

Salted Duck

Ingredients:

1 duck about 2,500 grams (5.5 lb)
150 grams (10 tbsp) cooking wine
80 grams (13 tsp) salt
20 grams (2/3 oz) scallions
5 grams (1/6 oz) ginger cut in chunks
20 grams (2/3 oz) fennel
20 grams (2/3 oz) cinnamon

Directions:

1. Dress the duck and rub its outside and inside with 50 g (8 tsp) of salt. Put it in a basin and let it marinate for 5 hours. Take out and wash off the salt.

2. Put the duck in water and, when the water starts to boil, take out the duck and wash it clean. Skim off the foam in the pot and put the duck back into the pot.

3. Put the sectioned scallions, ginger, fennel, cinnamon, and salt into the pot. Cover it up and again bring to a boil. Add the cooking wine and turn to a low fire to simmer for 40 minutes. When the duck becomes soft, take it out. Let it cool off and cut it into chunks. Pour on the original liquid and serve.

Features: The meat is tender and white.
Taste: Salty and delicious.

盐水鸭
Salted Duck

白切羊肉

主料：去骨羊腿肉 500 克

调料：酱油 10 克、葱 10 克、姜块 10 克、料酒 10 克

制作：①羊腿洗净，放入锅中加水烧沸，取出再洗去血沫，撇去汤中浮油沫。羊腿放回汤锅，加入葱、姜、料酒加盖烧沸，转文火烧约 2 小时。

②将羊肉捞出拣去葱、姜，待肉冷却后，切片装盘，浇上酱油即成。

特点：色艳

口味：咸鲜

Boiled Mutton in Salt

Ingredients:

500 grams (1.1 lb) boneless mutton leg
10 grams (1 1/2 tsp) soy sauce
10 grams (1/3 oz) sectioned scallions
10 grams (1/3 oz) ginger cut into chunks
10 grams (2 tsp) cooking wine

Directions:

1. Wash the meat and boil it in a pot. Take it out after the water boils to wash it clean. Skim off the foam in the pot and put the meat back in it. Add the scallions, ginger and cooking wine. Cover the pot and bring to a boil. Turn to low fire to simmer for 2 hours.

2. Take the meat out. Get rid of the scallions and ginger. When the meat is cool, cut it into slices and sprinkle on the soy sauce to serve.

Features: Looks very enticing with its colors of white meat and brownish soy sauce.

Taste: Salty and delicious.

白切羊肉
Boiled Mutton in Salt

沙司鱼片

主料：带皮鱼肉一段约 350 克

调料：油 1500 克（实耗 100 克）、糖 150 克、瓶装番茄酱 100 克、蒜茸 10 克、干淀粉 80 克、盐 2 克、料酒 5 克、水 50 克

制作：①将鱼肉段皮朝下放在砧扳上，用刀切成夹刀片（一刀切至皮连肉断，一刀切断），用料酒和 1 克盐腌渍 1 分钟，拍上干淀粉，并抖去余粉。

②将糖、盐 1 克、番茄酱、水一起放入碗中，拌和成调味汁。

③炒锅置旺火上烧热，放入油 1500 克，待油温八成热时，把鱼片放入油锅中炸至黄色捞出沥油。

④锅中留油 5 克，旺火烧热，投入蒜茸炒出香味，倒入调味汁，搅和成卤汁。将炸好的鱼倒入锅内，使鱼均匀吸取卤汁即成。

特点：色红有光泽

口味：甜中带酸

Sliced Fish with Tomato Sauce

Ingredients:

1 chunk of 350 grams (0.77 lb) of freshwater fish with the skin on
1,500 grams (3 cups) oil (only 100 g or 7 tbsp to be consumed)
150 grams (12 tbsp) sugar
100 grams (5 1/2 tbsp) tomato sauce
10 grams (1/3 oz) mashed garlic
80 grams (6 tbsp) dry cornstarch
2 grams (1/3 tsp) salt
5 grams (1 tsp) cooking wine
50 grams (3 tbsp) water

Directions:

1. Place the fish on a chopping board with the skin side down. Cut the meat deep all the way to the skin and, with the next cut, remove a section of fish. Repeat this process to cut the whole fish away from the skin. Marinate for 1 minute with the cooking wine and salt. Dust on the dry cornstarch and shake off the excess cornstarch.

2. Put the sugar, 1 g (1/6 tsp) of salt, tomato sauce and water in a bowl to make a sauce.

3. Heat the oil in a wok to 200-220 °C (390-430 °F). Deep-fry the fish chunks and bring them out to drain off the oil when they are golden yellow in color.

4. Keep 5 g (1 tsp) of oil in the wok and stir-fry the mashed garlic until it produces a distinctive aroma. Pour in the sauce and stir. Then put in the fish to allow the fish chunks to become evenly coated with the sauce. Now fish is ready to serve.

Features: Shiny red in color.
Taste: Sweet, with a sour touch.

沙司鱼片
Sliced Fish with Tomato Sauce

五香熏鱼

主料： 取鱼中段 500 克

调料： 油 1000 克（实耗 100 克）、料酒 85 克、酱油 50 克、糖 30 克、葱末 5 克、姜末 2.5 克、砂仁 2.5 克、茴香 2.5 克、五香粉 1 克

制作： ①将鱼洗净，横切成约 1 厘米宽的段，放碗中加酱油 25 克、料酒 35 克及茴香、砂仁拌均匀，腌渍约 2 小时，取出摊平，晾干。拣出香料备用。

②将腌鱼料汁倒入锅内，再加入料酒、酱油、糖及葱姜末，用中火烧沸，撇去浮末，离火。

③另取一锅置旺火上，倒入油，烧至八成热时，放入鱼块，炸至金黄捞出。约 2 分钟后油温再升至八成热时倒入鱼复炸，至外硬内嫩捞出。趁热将鱼放在盛卤汁的锅内翻拌，使鱼均匀吸收卤汁，约 2—3 分钟后倒出装盘，浇适量原卤汁，撒上五香粉即可。

特点： 外香脆，内鲜软

口味： 咸中带甜

Smoked Fish in Five Flavors

Ingredients:

500 grams (1.1 lb) freshwater fish (the middle part of a fish)
1,000 grams (2 cups) oil (only 100 g or 7 tbsp to be consumed)
85 grams (5 3/4 tbsp) cooking wine
50 grams (2 2/3 tbsp) soy sauce
30 grams (2 1/3 tbsp) sugar
5 grams (1/6 oz) finely cut scallions
2 1/2 grams (1/12 oz) chopped ginger
2 1/2 grams (1/12 oz) fennel
1 gram (1/5 tsp) five-flavor powder

Directions:

1. Cut the fish into sections 1 cm (0.4 inch) wide. Marinate for 2 hours with 25 g (1 1/2 tbsp) of soy sauce, 35 g (2 1/2 tbsp) of cooking wine and fennel in a bowl. Take fish out, lay it flat and let it dry out. Pick out the spices for later use.

2. Pour the sauce from marinating the fish into a pot. Add the remaining cooking wine, soy sauce, sugar, scallions and ginger and bring to a boil. Skim off the foam and turn off the fire.

3. Use another wok. Add the oil and heat to 200-220 °C (390-430 °F). Deep-fry the fish and take pieces out when they are golden yellow in color. Two minutes later, when the oil is back to 200-220 °C, deep-fry the fish pieces again until they are crispy on the outside. Put the fish in the pot with the sauce and stir well so that the fish fully absorbs the sauce. Take pieces out after 2 to 3 minutes. Place them on a plate, pour on some of the sauce from the pot and sprinkle on the five-flavor powder. Fish is now ready to serve.

Features: Crispy outside and tender inside.
Taste: Salty, with a slight sweet touch.

五香熏鱼
Smoked Fish in Five Flavors

白斩鸡

主料：活嫩母鸡 1 只约 1500 克

调料：料酒 100 克、盐 30 克、葱结 50 克、姜块 30 克、桂皮 10 克、大茴香 5 克、水 1500 克

制作：①将活鸡宰杀洗净，入沸水锅煮 5 分钟，捞出洗净。

②炒锅置旺火上，把葱、姜、桂皮、大茴香、水、料酒、盐、鸡一起放入，加盖置中火烧沸后，再移至微火上焖 1 小时取出，冷却后斩块，装盘浇上原汁。

特点：表皮油亮，肉呈白色

口味：鲜嫩

Boiled Tender Chicken in Soy Sauce

Ingredients:

1 live tender hen (about 1,500 g or 3.3 lb)
100 grams (7 tbsp) cooking wine
30 grams (5 tsp) salt
50 grams (1 2/3 oz) sectioned scallions
30 grams (1 oz) ginger chunks
10 grams (1/3 oz) cinnamon
5 grams (1/6 oz) aniseed
1500 grams (3 cups) water

Directions:

1. Kill the chicken. Dress it and boil it for 5 minutes.

2. Put the wok over a strong fire. Add the scallions, ginger, cinnamon, aniseed, water, cooking wine, salt and chicken. Cover the wok and bring to a boil. Turn to a low fire to simmer for 1 hour and then take chicken out. When it cools, cut into chunks and pour on the sauce from the wok.

Features: The skin is shiny and the meat is tender.
Taste: Very delicious.

白斩鸡
Boiled Tender Chicken in Soy Sauce

海米拌丝瓜

主料： 丝瓜 500 克

辅料： 海米 50 克

调料： 盐 2 克、味精 1 克、油 10 克、葱 5 克、姜 3 克、料酒 5 克

制作： ①丝瓜去皮洗净，切成长 5 厘米、宽 0.3 厘米的条。

②海米用清水洗净泡软。

③锅中放少许冷水烧沸，先倒入葱结、姜片、海米、料酒，煮沸后 2—3 分钟倒入丝瓜条，再煮沸出锅并滤去水，加盐、味精、油拌和装盘。

特点： 色艳爽口

口味： 咸鲜

Towel Gourd with Dried Shrimps

Ingredients:

500 grams (1.1 lb) towel gourd
50 grams (0.11 lb) dried shrimps
2 grams (1/3 tsp) salt
1 gram (1/4 tsp) MSG
10 grams (2 tsp) cooking oil
5 grams (1/6 oz) sectioned scallions
3 grams (1/10 oz) sliced ginger
5 grams (1 tsp) cooking wine

Directions:

1. Wash the towel gourd clean and cut into shreds 5 cm (2 inches) long and 0.3 cm (0.12 inch) wide.

2. Soak the dried shrimps in water.

3. Heat other water to a boiling point. Put in the scallions, ginger, shrimps, and cooking wine and boil for 2 to 3 minutes. Add the towel gourd and take out to drain when water boils again. Put salt and MSG onto the gourd and boil it again. Mix and serve.

Features: Beautifully colored and refreshing.
Taste: Salty.

海米拌丝瓜

Towel Gourd with Dried Shrimps

酒醉肉蟹

主料：活肉蟹10只约重1500克

调料：高度白酒500克、料酒500克、盐25克、花椒2.5克、桔皮25克、糖10克、姜片50克

制作：①将活蟹冲洗干净，滤干水，放入干净的小口大肚子的深容器内。

②将盐、糖溶化在白酒、料酒中后倒入容器内（须使酒浸没肉蟹），再放入花椒、桔皮、姜片，加盖密封，一周后即可食用（天热时缩短至3天）。

特点：酒香浓郁

口味：咸鲜

Drunken Crabs

Ingredients:

10 live crabs about 1,500 grams (3.3 lb)
500 grams (1 cup) strong liquor
500 grams (1 cup) cooking wine
25 grams (4 tsp) salt
2 1/2 grams (1/12 oz) Chinese prickly ash
25 grams (5/6 oz) dried orange peel
10 grams (2 tsp) sugar
50 grams (1 2/3 oz) sliced ginger

Directions:

1. Wash the crabs clean, drain off the water and put in a container with a small opening.

2. Let the salt and sugar dissolve in the liquor and wine and then pour the mixture into the container (to fully submerge the crabs). Add the Chinese prickly ash, orange peel, and ginger and put on the cover to fully seal. It will be ready to serve a week later. On hot days, it can be served 3 days later.

Features: Strongly aromatic from the liquor and wine.
Taste: Salty and delicious.

酒醉肉蟹
Drunken Crabs

凉拌葱油海蜇

主料：海蜇皮 500 克

调料：葱 10 克、盐 2 克、味精 1 克、糖 5 克、油 10 克

制作：①海蜇皮洗净切成丝状，用清水漂洗，滤去水，放入盆中，葱切末堆放在海蜇丝上。

②旺火热锅，加油烧至八成热，倒在葱末上，加盐、糖、味精拌和装盘。

特点：色泽鲜艳

口味：甜中带咸

Jellyfish in Scallion-flavored Sauce

Ingredients:

500 grams (1.1 lb) jellyfish
10 grams (1/3 oz) scallions
2 grams (1/3 tsp) salt
1 gram (1/4 tsp) MSG
5 grams (1 tsp) sugar
10 grams (2 tsp) cooking oil

Directions:

1. Wash the jellyfish clean and cut it into shreds. Put these in clean water in a basin. After a time take out, drain off the water and put back in the basin. Finely cut the scallions and put these on top of the shredded jellyfish.

2. Heat the oil in a wok to 200-220 °C (390-430 °F) and pour this onto the scallions and jellyfish. Add the salt, sugar and MSG. Mix and serve on a plate.

Features: Brightly colored.
Taste: Sweet with a salty touch.

凉拌葱油海蜇
Jelly Fish in Scallion-flavored Sauce

包菜丝

主料：包菜 500 克

调料：盐 2 克、糖 2 克、味精 1 克、腌红辣椒 2 只、油 10 克

制作：①包菜洗净切丝，红辣椒切丝。

②锅中冷水烧沸，倒入包菜丝煮沸捞起沥干水分，放入盆内，上面放红辣椒丝。

③旺火热锅，加入油烧至八九成热，浇在红辣椒丝上，加入盐、糖、味精拌和装盘。

特点：红绿相间，入口清爽

口味：味辣，鲜脆

Spicy Shredded Cabbage

Ingredients:

500 grams (1.1 lb) cabbage
2 grams (1/3 tsp) salt
2 grams (2/5 tsp) sugar
1 gram (1/4 tsp) MSG
2 pickled red chilies
10 grams (2 tsp) cooking oil

Directions:

1. Cut the cabbage and red chilies into shreds.

2. Heat water and bring it to a boil. Quick-boil the shredded cabbage, drain off the water and put in a basin. Sprinkle on the shredded chilies.

3. Heat the oil in a wok to around 220 °C (430 °F) and pour this on the red chilies and cabbage, Add the salt, sugar and MSG. Mix well and serve on a plate.

Features: Nice looking with the combination of green and red colors. Refreshing to the bite.

Taste: Spicy and crispy.

包菜丝
Spicy Shredded Cabbage

活炝虾

主料：活大虾 500 克

调料：高度白酒（或白兰地）50 克、红葡萄酒 100 克、香醋 10 克、葱末 10 克、姜末 5 克、酱油 20 克、盐 5 克、橙汁 10 克

制作：将活大虾洗净，放入容器里，加醋、盐、葱末、姜末、酱油、红葡萄酒、白酒、橙汁，摇匀搁置片刻装盘即可上桌。

特点：虾鲜活

口味：鲜嫩

Drunken Fresh Prawns

Ingredients:

500 grams (1.1 lb) live prawns
50 grams (3 tbsp) strong liquor
100 grams (6 tbsp) red wine
10 grams (2 tsp) vinegar
10 grams (1/3 oz) finely cut scallions
5 grams (1/6 oz) chopped ginger
20 grams (1 1/2 tbsp) soy sauce
5 grams (5/6 tsp) salt
10 grams (2 tsp) orange juice

Directions:

Wash the prawns clean and place them in a container. Add the vinegar, salt, scallions, ginger, soy sauce, red wine, liquor and orange juice. Shake well and put them aside for some moments before bringing them out on a plate to serve.

Features: Very fresh.
Taste: Tender and delicious.

活炝虾
Drunken Fresh Prawns

葱油萝卜丝

主料：白萝卜 500 克

调料：葱 20 克、糖 2 克、盐 2 克、味精 1 克、油 15 克

制作：①萝卜洗净去皮切成丝，葱切成末。萝卜丝放入碗中加盐 2 克，腌半小时，滤去水。

②旺火热锅，加入油烧至八成热。葱末放在萝卜丝上，浇上热油，加入糖，味精拌和装盘。

特点：色泽雪白

口味：爽口

Radish in Scallion-flavored Sauce

Ingredients:

500 grams (1.1 lb) white radishes
20 grams (2/3 oz) scallions
2 grams (2/5 tsp) sugar
2 grams (1/3 tsp) salt
1 gram (1/4 tsp) MSG
15 grams (1 tbsp) cooking oil

Directions:

1. Remove the skin from the radishes and cut them into thin shreds. Finely cut the scallions. Place the shredded radishes in a bowl. Add the salt and marinate for 30 minutes. Get rid of the juice from marinating.

2. Heat the oil in a wok to 200-220 °C (390-430 °F). Place the finely cut scallions on the shredded radishes, and pour on the heated oil. Add sugar and MSG. Mix and serve on a plate.

Features: As white as snow.
Taste: With a highly refreshing taste.

葱油萝卜丝
Radish in Scallion-flavored Sauce

红油鱼丝

主料：鱼肉一段 250 克

调料：料酒 2 克、盐 2 克、干淀粉 3 克、鸡蛋 1 个（用蛋清）、辣椒油 10 克

制作：①鱼肉去皮（将鱼皮朝下，肉向上，从中部下刀切至皮，然后紧贴鱼皮横刀向两旁片下鱼肉，然后反过来用同样的方法将肉与皮分离）。

②将鱼肉切成丝，加料酒、盐、鸡蛋清、干淀粉上浆备用。③炒锅放入冷水烧沸，放入上浆的鱼丝，煮沸捞起沥干水分，放入碗中。

④鱼丝中加入辣椒油拌和即可装盘。

特点：色爽肉嫩

口味：辣中带鲜

Shredded Fish with Spicy Oil

Ingredients:

1 piece of 250 grams (0.55 lb) freshwater fish
2 grams (2/5 tsp) cooking wine
2 grams (1/3 tsp) salt
3 grams (1 1/2 tsp) dry cornstarch
1 egg (only use the egg white)
10 grams (2 tsp) spicy oil

Directions:

1. Remove the fish skin by placing the fish skin side down and cutting in the middle deep to the skin. Then continue to cut side ways to separate the meat from the skin.

2. Cut the fish into shreds and place these in a bowl. Add the cooking wine, salt, egg white, and dry cornstarch.

3. Heat water and then quick-boil the coated fish shreds. Take out, drain off the water and put the fish shreds in a bowl.

4. Add the spicy oil and mix before serving.

Features: The meat is tender and refreshing.
Taste: Spicy and delicious.

红油鱼丝
Shredded Fish with Spicy Oil

凉拌豇豆

主料：长豇豆 200 克

调料：盐 1 克、味精 1 克、油 5 克

制作：①长豇豆洗净，切成长 0.5 厘米的段，锅内放水烧沸，倒入豇豆，氽 3 分钟捞出滤干水份。

②豇豆置盆中，加盐、味精，旺火热锅加油烧热，浇在豇豆上拌和装盘。

特点：色翠绿

口味：咸鲜

Crispy Cow Peas

Ingredients:

200 grams (0.44 lb) cow peas
1 gram (1/6 tsp) salt
1 gram (1/4 tsp) MSG
5 grams (1 tsp) oil

Directions:

1. Wash the cow peas clean and cut into sections 0.5 cm (0.2 inch) long. Boil them for 3 minutes. Take out and drain off the water.

2. Put the cow peas in a basin, add the salt and MSG. Heat the oil to around 200 °C (390 °F) and pour on the cow peas.

Features: Invitingly green
Taste: Salty and refreshing.

凉拌豇豆
Crispy Cow Peas

水晶鱼冻

主料：鱼 500 克

辅料：琼脂 10 克、绿叶菜 5 克、熟火腿 5 克

调料：料酒 25 克、盐 15 克、葱汁 10 克、姜汁 10 克、水 1000 克

制作：①将鱼洗净，去刺和皮，切成粒状置碗中，加料酒、盐、葱汁、姜汁拌和，锅中水烧沸放入鱼粒，2 分钟后捞出滤去水放入碗中，鱼汤留用。琼脂用水浸泡，洗净后切细，加入鱼汤。

②在 6 只小碗中分别倒入 1 匙鱼汤，放入冰箱 5 分钟后取出。在每碗结冻的鱼汤上用绿叶菜，火腿片拼成花形，再加满鱼粒和原汤后再放入冰箱结冻，5 - 8 分钟后取出倒扣在盘中。

特点：晶莹如脂玉

口味：鲜凉爽嫩，入口即化

Crystal Fish

Ingredients:

500 grams (1.1 lb) freshwater fish
10 grams (2 tsp) agar
5 grams (1/6 oz) green vegetables
5 grams (1/6 oz) cooked ham
25 grams (1 3/4 tbsp) cooking wine
15 grams (2 1/2 tsp) salt
10 grams (2 tsp) scallion juice
10 grams (2 tsp) ginger juice
1000 grams (2 cups) water

Directions:

1. Wash the fish clean, remove the bones and skin, and cut into small dices. Place these in a bowl. Add the cooking wine, salt, scallion juice, ginger juice and mix. Boil the fish dices for 2 minutes. Take out, drain off the water and put it into a bowl. Soak the agar in fresh water, wash clean and cut into fine shreds. Add the agar shreds to the fish soup. Cut the vegetables into sections. Slice the ham.

2. Put one tsp of fish soup in each of six small bowls, and cool in the refrigerator for 5 minutes before taking out. Make beautiful patterns with the green vegetables and sliced ham on top of the fish soup in the bowls. Add the fish dices and original soup to the brim of the bowls and put them back again in the refrigerator. Take out 5 to 8 minutes later and put upside down on a plate.

Features: As crystal as jade.
Taste: Cold, refreshing and delicious.

水晶鱼冻
Crystal Fish

辣白菜

主料：嫩白菜梗 500 克

调料：干红辣椒 2 只、姜丝 10 克、盐 10 克、糖 60 克、白醋 25 克、油 20 克、水 1000 克

制作：①将白菜洗净，顺筋切 5 厘米长，0.5 厘米宽的条，放入盆内，撒上盐 10 克，加盖腌 4 小时，取出滤去水，放入盆中。红辣椒切丝。

②旺火热锅，加油后，放入红辣椒略炒，再倒入水、糖和姜丝用勺搅和，烧沸后放醋。将料汁倒入白菜盆中，加盖浸 4 小时即可上桌。

特点：色艳，脆嫩爽口

口味：酸甜微辣

Spicy Chinese Cabbage

Ingredients:

500 grams (1.1 lb) outer leaves of tender Chinese cabbage
2 dried red chilies
10 grams (1/3 oz) ginger shredded
10 grams (1 2/3 tsp) salt
60 grams (4 2/3 tbsp) sugar
25 grams (1 2/3 tbsp) vinegar
20 grams (1 1/2 tbsp) oil
1000 grams (2 cups) water

Directions:

1. Wash the cabbage clean and cut it along the grain into shreds 5 cm (2 inches) long and 0.5 cm (0.2 inch) wide. Put in a basin. Add 10 g (1 2/3 tsp) of salt and put on the cover to let cabbage marinate for 4 hours. Take out, remove the liquid and put the cabbage back in the basin. Cut the red chilies into thin shreds.

2. Heat the oil to 180-200 °C (3555-390 °F) and stir-fry the red chilies. Add water, sugar and ginger. Stir well, and when it starts to boil, add the vinegar and turn off the fire. Pour this sauce into the basin with the cabbage. Put on the cover and marinate another 4 hours before serving.

Features: Brightly colored, crispy and refreshing to the bite.

Taste: Sweet, sour and spicy.

辣白菜
Spicy Chinese Cabbage

糖拌西红柿

主料： 西红柿200克

调料： 糖20克

制作： ①西红柿洗净，用开水烫透去皮（也可不去皮）。②将西红柿一切两半，然后切成薄片装盘，撒上糖腌半小时即可食用。

特点： 色艳

口味： 甜中带酸

Sweet Tomatoes

Ingredients:

200 grams (0.44 lb) tomatoes
20 grams (1 1/2 tbsp) sugar

Directions:

1. Wash the tomatoes clean. (Optional: pour hot water on the tomatoes to remove the skin)
2. Cut each of the tomatoes into two halves and then cut them into thin slices. Put these on a plate, sprinkle on the sugar and it is ready to serve.

Features: Brightly colored.
Taste: Sweet with a sour touch.

糖拌西红柿
Sweet Tomatoes

蒜末拌黄瓜

主料： 黄瓜 300 克

调料： 蒜头 20 克、油 10 克、味精 1 克、糖 1 克、盐 3 克

制作： ①黄瓜洗净去籽，切成 0.3 厘米厚的薄片，放在盘中，撒上盐腌半小时，滤去水，放入原盘中

②蒜头去皮切末，放在黄瓜上面，旺火热锅，加油烧熟浇在蒜末上，再加味精、糖拌和装盘。

特点： 色艳爽口

口味： 咸鲜有蒜香

Cucumbers with Garlic

Ingredients:

300 grams (0.66 lb) cucumbers
20 grams (2/3 oz) garlic
10 grams (2 tsp) oil
1 gram (1/4 tsp) MSG
1 gram (1/5 tsp) sugar
3 grams (1/2 tsp) salt

Directions:

1. Wash the cucumbers clean, get rid of the seeds and cut the cucumbers into slices 0.3 cm (0.12 inch) thick. Put them on a plate, sprinkle on the salt and marinate for 30 minutes. Get rid of the liquid from the marinating.

2. Remove the skin of the garlic cloves, crush them and place on top of the cucumbers. Heat the oil in a wok to 180-200 °C (355-390 °F) and pour on the crushed garlic. Add the MSG, mix well and put on a serving plate.

Features: Brightly colored and refreshing to the bite.
Taste: Salty with the aroma of garlic.

蒜末拌黄瓜
Cucumbers with Garlic

盐水虾

主料：活大虾 500 克

调料：葱结 10 克、姜块 5 克、料酒 25 克、清水 1000 克、盐 6 克

制作：①锅中放水 1000 克，放入葱结、姜块、盐烧沸后，倒入虾，加料酒烧至虾断生即捞出。

②原清汤拣去葱、姜，滤清凉透，再放入虾，浸 15 分钟即成。

特点：色红

口味：咸中带鲜

Salted Prawns

Ingredients:

500 grams (1.1 lb) live prawns
10 grams (1/3 oz) sectioned scallions
5 grams (1/6 oz) ginger cut into chunks
25 grams (1 3/4 tbsp) cooking wine
1,000 grams (2 cups) water
6 grams (1 tsp) salt

Directions:

1. Put the water in a pot, add the scallions, ginger, and salt and bring to a boil. Put in the prawns. Add the cooking wine and, once the prawns are done, take out.

2. Get rid of the scallions and ginger from the liquid and let it cool off. Put the prawns back into the liquid to soak for 5 minutes and they are ready to serve.

Features: Beautiful red color.
Taste: Salty and delicious.

盐水虾
Salted Prawns

麻辣鸡丝

主料：生鸡脯肉 250 克

调料：麻油 3 克、葱 5 克、姜片 2 克、麻辣鲜 5 克（超市有卖)、盐 2 克、味精 1 克

制作：将生鸡脯肉洗净，锅中加水放入葱、姜、鸡脯，烧 30 分钟，捞出鸡脯凉透，切成细丝，加麻油、盐、味精、麻辣鲜拌和装盘上席。

特点：鲜香

口味：咸鲜麻辣

Chicken in Chili and Peppery Sauce

Ingredients：

250 grams (0.55 lb) chicken breast
3 grams (3/5 tsp) sesame oil
5 grams (1/6 oz) sectioned scallions
2 grams (1/15 oz) sliced ginger
5 grams (1 tsp) spicy and peppery sauce (which can be found in Chinese grocery stores)
2 grams (1/3 tsp) salt
1 gram (1/4 tsp) MSG
750 grams (1 1/2 cups) water

Directions：

Put the water in a pot, add scallions, ginger and chicken breast to cook for 30 minutes. Take the chicken breast out. Let it cool off and then cut into fine shreds. Add the sesame oil, salt, MSG and the spicy and peppery sauce. Mix well and it is ready to serve.

Features： Strongly aromatic.

Taste： Salty, spicy, peppery and delicious.

麻辣鸡丝
Chicken with Chili & Peppery Sauce

油焖春笋

主料：春笋1250克

调料：油750克（实耗75克）、酱油60克、糖25克、味精2克、料酒5克、麻油10克、水200克

制作：①春笋除去外皮壳，洗净，一剖两半，后再斜刀切成5厘米长、2厘米宽的块。

②旺火热锅，加油，烧至五成热时，倒入笋块炸至浅黄色捞出。

③原锅留油30克，放入笋、料酒、酱油翻炒，然后加水、糖烧沸，加盖改用小火焖5分钟，转旺火收稠，加味精淋芝麻油即可颠翻出锅。

特点：笋脆嫩

口味：咸中带甜

Spring Bamboo Shoots in Light Sauce

Ingredients:

1,250 grams (2.75 lb) spring bamboo shoots
750 grams (1 1/2 cups) oil (only 1/10 to be consumed)
60 grams (3 tbsp) soy sauce
25 grams (2 tbsp) sugar
2 grams (1/2 tsp) MSG
5 grams (1 tsp) cooking wine
10 grams (2 tsp) sesame oil
200 grams (2/5 cup) water

Directions:

1. Remove the outer skin of the bamboo shoots. Wash them clean and cut each into two halves. Then cut in a slanting way into chunks 5 cm (2 inches) long and 2 cm (0.8 inch) wide.

2. Heat the oil in a wok to 110-135 °C (230-275 °F) and deep-fry the bamboo shoots until they are light yellow in color.

3. Keep 30 g (2 tbsp) of oil in the wok. Add the bamboo shoots, cooking wine and soy sauce, and stir-fry. Add water and sugar and bring to a boil. Put on the wok lid and simmer for 5 minutes. Turn to a strong fire to boil off some of the liquid. Add the MSG and sprinkle on the sesame oil. Turn over, bring out and put on a plate to serve.

Features: Bamboo shoots are tender and crispy.
Taste: Salty with a sweet touch.

油焖春笋
Spring Bamboo Shoots in Light Sauce

椒盐花生米

主料：花生米 250 克

调料：油 800 克（实耗 30 克）、花椒盐 10 克（自选市场有成品卖）

制作：①如自己加工花椒盐可将花椒洗净，用铁锅文火炒熟，趁热碾碎，加与花椒等量的盐调用。

②将花生米和油一起放入锅中，用文火慢慢炸熟，捞出装盘，撒花椒盐，散热后即可食用。

特点：香脆

口味：椒盐味浓

Peanuts with Pepper Salt

Ingredients:

250 grams (0.55 lb) peanuts

800 grams (1 3/5 cup) oil (only 30 g or 2 tbsp to be consumed)

10 grams (2 tsp) pepper salt

Directions:

1. Either buy the pepper salt at a grocery store or make it by baking and then grinding Chinese prickly ash and mixing that with salt at a ratio of 1/2 prickly ash and 1/2 salt.

2. Put the peanuts and oil in a wok over a low fire to gradually roast the peanuts. Take out and put on a plate. Sprinkle on the pepper salt. When the dish cools off, it is ready to serve.

Features: Crispy and aromatic.

Taste: Strong peppery and salty taste.

椒盐花生米
Peanuts with Pepper Salt

雪菜毛豆子

主料：雪菜（俗名雪里蕻）75 克、速冻青毛豆子 50 克

调料：水 150 克、油 30 克、味精 1 克、麻油 10 克、盐 1 克、糖 5 克

制作：①雪菜洗净，切成末。毛豆子解冻，过水冲洗，并滤干水份。

②旺火热锅，加油烧至五成热时，将毛豆子倒入翻炒后加水、盐、糖烧沸，下雪菜末炒 2 分钟加味精，淋麻油出锅（市面上出售的大都是盐渍过或加工过的雪菜，故加盐时需根据自己的口味）

特点：色泽鲜绿，清淡爽口

口味：咸鲜

Pickled Mustard Leaves with Green Peas

Ingredients:

75 grams (0.165 lb) pickled mustard leaves
50 grams (0.11 lb) fast-frozen green peas
150 grams (10 tbsp) water
30 grams (2 tbsp) oil
1 gram (1/4 tsp) MSG
10 grams (2 tsp) sesame oil
1 gram (1/6 tsp) salt
5 grams (1 tsp) sugar

Directions:

1. Wash the pickled mustard leaves clean and cut them into tiny sections. Defrost the peas, wash them clean and drain off the water.

2. Heat the oil to 110-135 °C (230-275 °F). Stir-fry the peas for 1 minute and add the water, salt and sugar. Bring it to a boil. Add the pickled mustard leaves to cook for 2 minutes. Put in the MSG and sprinkle on the sesame oil. Take out to serve.

Features: Tender green in color, refreshing to the bite.

Taste: Salty and delicious.

雪菜毛豆子
Pickled Mustard Leaves with Green Peas

麻油拌苦瓜

主料：苦瓜 250 克

辅料：胡萝卜 10 克

调料：盐 2 克、味精 1 克、麻油 10 克

制作：①苦瓜洗净，剖开，去籽切片，胡萝卜也洗净切片。

②锅中冷水烧开，倒入苦瓜，葫萝卜焯水，倒出滤干水份后，加盐、味精、麻油拌和装盘。

特点：红绿相映、清淡爽口

口味：苦中带鲜

Balsam Pear with Sesame Oil

Ingredients:

250 grams (0.55 lb) balsam pear
10 grams (1/3 oz) carrot
2 grams (1/3 tsp) salt
1 gram (1/4 tsp) MSG
10 grams (2 tsp) sesame oil
500 grams (1 cup) water

Directions:

1. Wash the balsam pear clean, take out the pulp and seeds, cut into thin slices. Cut the carrot into slices too.

2. Bring the water to boil and put in the balsam pear and carrot to quick-boil. Take out and drain off the water. Add the salt, MSG and sesame oil. Mix and serve.

Features: Beautiful combination of green and red colors. Refreshing to eat.
Taste: Bitter and refreshing.

麻油拌苦瓜
Balsam Pear with Sesame Oil

油焖茭白

主料：茭白 500 克

调料：油 50 克、盐 3 克、糖 2 克、味精 1 克、水 150 克、酱油 5 克

制作：①茭白去壳洗净，切长 10 厘米，宽 1 厘米的条。②中火热锅，下油将茭白煸炒后放入酱油、水、盐、糖烧沸，加盖转小火焖 10 分钟后，加入味精，稍收干汤汁即可出锅，冷却后装盘。

特点：清香

口味：咸中带甜

Shredded Wild Rice Stems

Ingredients:

500 grams (1.1 lb) wild rice stems
50 grams (3 1/2 tbsp) oil
3 grams (1/2 tsp) salt
2 grams (2/5 tsp) sugar
1 gram (1/4 tsp) MSG
150 grams (10 tbsp) water
5 grams (1 tsp) soy sauce

Directions:

1. Remove the outer skin of the wild rice stems and cut into sections 10 cm (4 inches) long and 1 cm (0.4 inch) wide.

2. Heat the oil to 70-100 ˚C (160-210 ˚F) and quick-stir-fry the wild rice stem sections. Then add the soy sauce, water, salt and sugar, and bring to a boil. Cover the wok to simmer for 10 minutes. Add the MSG, boil off some of the liquid over a strong fire. Take out and serve.

Features: Refreshingly aromatic.
Taste: Salty with a sweet touch.

油焖茭白
Shredded Wild Rice Stems

盐水青毛豆

主料：青毛豆 250 克

调料：盐 15 克、味精 2 克、八角 5 克、茴香 2 克、水 1000 克

制作：毛豆洗净两头剪去，锅中加水烧沸，放入盐、八角、茴香和毛豆煮 20 分钟加入味精，离火浸 30 分钟后装盘即可。(用同样的方法处理带壳花生可做出“盐水花生”)

特点：色翠绿

口味：咸鲜

Boiled Salted Young Soy Beans

Ingredients：

250 grams (0.55 lb) young soy beans with the shells on
15 grams (2 1/2 tsp) salt
2 grams (1/2 tsp) MSG
5 grams (1/6 oz) aniseed
2 grams (1/15 oz) fennel
1000 grams (2 cups) water

Directions：

Wash the soy beans clean and cut off both ends so as to allow them to absorb the liquid during boiling. Put the water in a pot, bring to a boil, add the salt, aniseed, fennel, and young soy beans to boil for 20 minutes. Add the MSG and turn off the fire to soak for 30 minutes. Put on a plate to serve. (The same method can be used to cook “Boiled Salty Peanuts”.)

Features： Tenderly green in color.
Taste： Salty and delicious.

盐水青毛豆
Boiled Salty Young Soy Beans

凉拌西瓜条

主料：西瓜皮 500 克

辅料：腌红辣椒 2 只

调料：盐 8 克、糖 2 克、味精 1 克、麻油 10 克

制作：西瓜皮去外皮洗净，切成条，放入盘中加盐腌半小时，滤去水，腌红辣椒切丝，放在瓜条上面。再撒入糖、味精、麻油与瓜皮拌和即可。

特点：悦目爽口

口味：咸鲜

Watermelon Peel with Red Chilies

Ingredients:

500 grams (1.1 lb) whitish skin of watermelon
2 pickled red chilies
8 grams (1 1/3 tsp) salt
2 grams (2/5 tsp) sugar
1 gram (1/4 tsp) MSG
10 grams (2 tsp) sesame oil

Directions:

Wash the watermelon clean and remove the outer skin. Cut into sections under 4 cm (1.6 inches) long and 0.6 cm (0.24 inch) wide. Cut the red chilies into thin shreds. Marinate with the salt for 30 minutes in a bowl. Get rid of the liquid from marinating, spread the red chili shreds on the watermelon peel, add sugar, MSG and sesame oil, and serve.

Features: Inviting to look at and refreshing.
Taste: Salty and delicious.

凉拌西瓜条
Watermelon Peels with Red Chilies

香干拌西芹

主料：西芹 500 克
辅料：香干 30 克
调料：糖 10 克、盐 2 克、味精 1 克、色拉油 10 克
制作：①西芹洗净切丝，香干切丝，锅内放冷水烧沸放入西芹和香干，煮沸捞起沥干水份，放入盆中。
②旺火热锅，加入油烧八成热，浇在西芹和香干上再加入糖、盐、味精、色拉油拌和即可。
特点：色艳
口味：鲜香

Celery with Bean Curd Cheese

Ingredients:
500 grams (1.1 lb) celery
30 grams (1 oz) bean curd cheese
10 grams (2 tsp) sugar
2 grams (1/3 tsp) salt
1 gram (1/4 tsp) MSG
10 grams (2 tsp) salad oil

Directions:
1. Cut the celery on a slant into shreds. Quick-boil these along with bean curd cheese which should also be cut into shreds of preferable thickness. When the water boils, take out, drain off the water and place in a bowl.

2. Heat the oil in a wok to 200-220 °C (390-430 °F) and pour on the celery and bean curd cheese. Add the salt, sugar, MSG and salad oil. Mix well and serve.

Features: Brightly colored.
Taste: Delicious.

香干拌西芹
Celery with Bean Curd Cheese

拌土豆丝

主料：土豆 250 克

调料：油 10 克、葱末 5 克、盐 3 克、味精 1 克、水 400 克

制作：①土豆去皮洗净，切成丝，放水中漂洗干净后备用

②锅中加水 400 克烧沸，倒入土豆丝煮沸捞起滤干水份放入盆中，加盐、味精、油拌和，再撒上葱末即可。

特点：色淡黄，入口爽脆

口味：咸鲜

Shredded Potatoes in Light Sauce

Ingredients:

250 grams (0.55 lb) potatoes
10 grams (2 tsp) oil
5 grams (1/6 oz) finely cut scallions
3 grams (1/2 tsp) salt
1 gram (1/4 tsp) MSG
400 grams (4/5 cup) water

Directions:

1. Remove the skin of the potatoes. Cut into thin shreds, soak in water and take out.

2. Put the water in a pot and boil the potato shreds. When the pot fully boils, take out the shredded potatoes, drain off the water and put potato shreds in a basin. Add the salt, MSG and oil, and mix well. Put in the finely cut scallions and it is ready to serve.

Features: Light yellow in color and crispy.
Taste: Salty and delicious.

拌土豆丝
Shredded Potatoes in Light Sauce

鹅肫

主料：鹅肫（鸡、鸭肫亦可）五只约400克

调料：盐25克、料酒25克、葱10克、姜10克、花椒10粒

制作：①鹅肫洗净放入盆中，用盐15克拌和，加花椒10粒腌10小时。

②取出鹅肫用水洗净，入冷水锅中烧沸，捞出洗净，原锅中留汤500克，放入盐10克，葱、姜、料酒和肫烧开后，转小火烧40分钟，倒入盆中，冷却后切片装盘浇原卤上席。

特点：肫脆香鲜

口味：咸鲜，卤汁味醇

Goose Gizzard

Ingredients:

5 goose (or duck or chicken) gizzards, about 400 grams (0.88 lb)
25 grams (4 tsp) salt
25 grams (1 3/4 tsp) cooking wine
10 grams (1/3 oz) sectioned scallions
10 grams (1/3 oz) sliced ginger
10 grains of Chinese prickly ash
750 grams (1 1/2 cups) water

Directions:

1. Wash the gizzards clean and put in a basin to marinate for 10 hours with 15 g (2 1/2 tsp) of salt and Chinese prickly ash.

2. Wash the gizzards again and boil in a pot. When the pot is fully boiling, take the gizzards out and wash them clean again. Keep 500 g (1 cup) of water in the pot. Add 10 g (1 2/3 tsp) of salt, scallions, ginger, cooking wine and the gizzards. Bring to a boil. Turn the fire to low and simmer for 40 minutes. Pour into a basin. When they have cooled off, cut them into slices and put on a plate. Pour on the sauce from the pot and it is ready to serve.

Features: Strongly aromatic.

Taste: Delicious and richly flavored.

鹅肫
Goose Gizzard

糟鸡

主料：活嫩鸡 1 只约 1000 克

调料：香糟 100 克、盐 45 克、葱 30 克、姜 18 克、花椒 24 克、水 2000 克

制作：①鸡宰杀退毛去内脏洗净，锅中加水 2000 克，放入鸡、葱 10 克、姜 6 克、盐 15 克，烧沸后转小火烧 40 分钟捞出。热鸡汤内放花椒、盐 30 克、葱 20 克、姜 12 克，待冷却后再加入香糟，放入鸡浸 20 分钟。

②熟鸡分斩 4 块，放入盆中。然后将糟卤用纱布过滤，倒入放有鸡块的盆中加盖置冰箱中，2 小时后取出鸡块，用刀切小后装盘，浇上原卤汁。

特点：色泽纯白

口味：糟香入味，咸中带鲜

Chicken with Distillers' Grain

Ingredients:

1 live tender chicken about 1,000 grams (2.2 lb)
100 grams (0.22 lb) distillers' grain
45 grams (7 1/2 tsp) salt
30 grams (1 oz) sectioned scallions
18 grams (3/5 oz) sliced ginger
24 grams (4/5 oz) Chinese prickly ash
2000 grams (4 cups) water

Directions:

1. Slaughter the chicken, dress it and remove the inside. Wash it clean. Put the water in a pot and then put in the chicken, 10 g (1/3 oz) of scallions, 6 g (1/5 oz) of ginger and 15 g (2 1/2 tsp) of salt, and bring to a boil. Turn to a low fire to simmer for 40 minutes and take out. Add the Chinese prickly ash, and the remaining salt, scallions and ginger into the liquid while it is still warm. When it cools off, add the distiller's grain and let the chicken soak for 20 minutes.

2. Cut the chicken into four parts and place in a basin. Let the distillers' grain alcohol go through a filter to get rid of any residue. Put the liquid from this process into the basin with the chicken and place in the refrigerator. Take out 2 hours later. Cut into small chunks and put on a plate. Pour on the original liquid from the pot and it is ready to serve.

Features: Pure white in color.

Taste: With a rich flavor of the distillers' grain. Salty and delicious.

糟鸡
Chicken with Distillers' Grain

糖醋藕片

主料：藕 500 克

调料：糖 100 克、白醋 10 克、水 100 克

制作：①将藕洗净沿横断面切成 0.3 厘米厚薄片，放在水中漂清滤去水份放入盆中。

②炒锅置火上，倒入水，加糖，烧沸熬至稠浓后再放入白醋，一起倒入藕片中，泡 1 小时后，即可食用。

特点：色泽雪白，脆嫩爽口

口味：甜中带酸

Sweet and Sour Lotus Root Siices

Ingredients:

500 grams (1.1 lb) lotus root
100 grams (7 2/3 tbsp) sugar
10 grams (2 tsp) white vinegar
100 grams (6 tbsp) water

Directions:

1. Wash the lotus root clean and cut it across the grain into slices 0.3 cm (0.12 inch) thick. Wash clean again, drain off the water and put in a basin.

2. Put water in the pot. Add sugar and bring to a boil. When the sauce thickens, add the vinegar and the lotus root and soak for 1 hour. Then it is ready to serve.

Features: Snow white in color, crispy and soothing to the mouth.
Taste: Sweet with a sour touch.

糖醋藕片
Sweet and Sour Lotus Root Slices

五香酱牛肉

主料： 牛肉 500 克

调料： 葱 10 克、姜 5 克、料酒 25 克、酱油 10 克、糖 5 克、桂皮 5 克、甘草 5 克、大茴香 15 克、丁香 2 粒、水 300 克

制作： ①牛肉洗净切块用酒，酱油、盐、葱、姜、香料拌匀，放冰箱中腌渍约 1 小时。

②将腌好的牛肉和调料一起加水烧沸后，转小火焖 1 小时捞出，待其冷却后切成薄片装盘。

特点： 色泽深褐

口味： 五香味浓

Five-flavored Beef

Ingredients:

500 grams (1.1 lb) tender beef
10 grams (1/3 oz) sectioned scallions
5 grams (1/6 oz) sliced ginger
25 grams (1 3/4 tbsp) cooking wine
10 grams (1 1/2 tsp) soy sauce
5 grams (1 tsp) sugar
5 grams (1/6 oz) cinnamon
5 grams (1/6 oz) licorice root
15 grams (1/2 oz) aniseed
2 grains of clove
300 grams (3/5 cup) water

Directions:

1. Cut the beef into large chunks, add the cooking wine, soy sauce, salt, scallions, ginger and other spices. Mix well and marinate for 1 hour in the refrigerator.

2. Add the water to the marinated beef with the spices and bring to a boil. When it starts to boil, turn to a low fire to simmer for 1 hour. Take the beef out and when it cools off, cut into slices. Put on a plate and serve.

Features: Dark brown in color.
Taste: Richly flavored.

五香酱牛肉
Five-flavor Beef

美味羊糕

主料：带皮去骨羊腿肉 1000 克

辅料：白萝卜 200 克

调料：酱油 20 克、盐 8 克、糖 10 克、葱 20 克、姜块 5 克、料酒 50 克、蒜头 10 克、甜面酱 10 克

制作：①羊腿肉刮洗干净，切 2 厘米见方的小块，放入锅中加水（以浸没羊肉为准）烧沸，取出洗净。撇去汤中浮沫，加入酱油、盐、糖、料酒烧沸，再放入羊肉、白萝卜（切大块，拍松）、葱、姜，加盖烧沸，转文火煮三小时至酥烂。

②拣去白萝卜、葱、姜，撇去浮油，转旺火稍收稠汤汁。倒入 3.5 厘米深的平底盘内，再将汤汁浇在上面，待其冷冻后切成长 8 厘米、宽 2 厘米、厚 0.7 厘米的片装盘。

③蒜头洗净去皮，与甜面酱分别装入小碟，随羊糕同时上桌。羊糕佐以蒜头甜面酱味道更好。

特点：色泽红褐

口味：咸鲜

Fragrant Jelly Mutton

Ingredients:

1,000 grams (2.2 lb) boneless mutton
200 grams (0.44 lb) white radish
20 grams (1 tbsp) soy sauce
8 grams (1 1/3 tsp) salt
10 grams (2 tsp) sugar
20 grams (2/3 oz) sectioned scallions
5 grams (1/6 oz) ginger chunks
50 grams (3 1/3 tbsp) cooking wine
10 grams (1/3 oz) garlic
10 grams (1 1/2 tsp) sweet bean paste

Directions:

1. Cut the mutton into square chunks 2 cm (0.8 inch) long on each side. Put these in a pot and add water until the mutton is totally submerged. Bring to a boil and take out to wash clean. Skim the foam off the liquid. Add the soy sauce, salt, sugar, and cooking wine, and bring to a boil. Add the mutton, radish (cut into chunks and crushed with a heavy Chinese kitchen chopper), scallions, and ginger, and cover the pot. When liquid boils, turn to a low fire to cook for 3 hours.

2. Pick out and remove the radish, scallions, and ginger. Also remove the oil drifting on top of the liquid. Turn to a strong fire to boil off some of the liquid. Put the mutton in a flat-bottomed pot 3.5 cm (1.4 inches) deep. Pour on the liquid. When it cools to a jelly form, cut the mutton and jelly together into slices 8 cm (3.2 inches) long, 2 cm (0.8 inch) wide and 0.7 (0.28 inch) thick. Put them on a plate.

3. Put the garlic and sweet bean paste in two separate small plates and serve together with the jellied mutton to enrich the flavor.

Features: Shiny and reddish in color.
Taste: Salty and delicious.

美味羊糕
Fragrant Jelly Mutton

计量换算表

1磅	1盎司	1打兰	1格令
约454克	约28克	约1.8克	约0.06克

调料 ml 勺	水	油	酱油	醋	料酒	盐	味精	砂糖	淀粉
1ml勺	约1克	约0.9克	约1.2克	约1克	约1克	约1.2克	约0.7克	约0.9克	约0.4克
5ml勺	约5克	约4.5克	约6克	约5克	约5克	约6.3克	约3.7克	约4.5克	约2克
15ml勺	约15克	约13.5克	约18克	约15克	约15克	约18.5克	约11克	约13克	约6克
50ml勺	约50克	约55克	约60克	约50克	约50克	约63克		约42克	约20克
500ml勺	约500克	约549克	约600克	约500克	约500克	约630克			

A comparison of the weight systems

US system	1 grain(gr)	1ounce(oz)	1pound(lb)
Metric	0.065 gram(g)	28.35 grams(g)	454 grams(g)

A conversion table for measuring Chinese cooking ingredients*

ingredients cornstarch	water	ckg oil	soy sauce	vinegar	ckg wine	salt	MSG	sugar	cornstarch
1 pinch/1ml	1g	0.9g	1.2g	1g	1g	1.2g	0.7g	0.9g	0.4g
1tsp/5ml	5g	4.5g	6g	5g	5g	6.3g	3.7g	4.5g	2g
1tbsp/15ml	15g	13.5g	18g	15g	15g	18.5g	11g	13g	6g
1.76floz/50ml	50g	55g	60g	50g	50g	63g		42g	20g
3.52floz/1cup	500g	549g	600g	500g	500g	630g			

*All figures in grams given here are approximate as the exact equivalents will result in too many digits after the decimal point.

在编辑《学做中国菜》系列丛书的过程中，得到了苏州饭店的大力支持和帮助。作为苏州市旅游业的骨干企业苏州饭店已有数十年的历史，饭店拥有一流的烹饪厨师，经验丰富，技艺精湛。今借此书出版之机，我们对苏州饭店给予的支持，深表感谢!

We wish to thank the Suzhou Hotel, which kindly provided strong support and assistance to the compilation of the *Learn to Cook Chinese Dishes* series. As a major tourist hotel in the city of Suzhou, the Suzhou Hotel has a history of dozens of years and is serviced by experienced first-class chefs.

图书在版编目(CIP)数据
学做中国菜·冷菜类:汉、英对照/《学做中国菜》编委会编.-北京:外文出版社,2000
ISBN 7-119-02517-1

Ⅰ.学… Ⅱ.学… Ⅲ.冷菜-烹饪-中国-汉、英对照 Ⅳ.TS972.1
中国版本图书馆 CIP 数据核字(1999)第 70473 号

Members of the Editorial Board:
Sun Jiaping Lu Qinpu
Sun Shuming Liu Chun'gen
Lan Peijin
Dish preparation and text:
Zhu Deming Wen Jinshu
Zhu Guifu Zhang Guomin
Zhang Guoxiang Xu Rongming
Cao Gang
Editor: Lan Peijin
English translation and editing:
Huang Youyi Foster Stockwell Cong Guoling
Design: Lan Peijin
Photography: Sun Shuming Liu Chun'gen Lan Peijin
Cover design: Wang Zhi

编委: 孙建平 鲁钦甫 孙树明
刘春根 兰佩瑾
菜肴制作及撰文: 朱德明 温金树
朱桂福 张国民
张国祥 徐荣明
曹 刚
责任编辑: 兰佩瑾
英文翻译: 黄友义 卓柯达 丛国玲
设计: 兰佩瑾
摄影: 孙树明 刘春根 兰佩瑾
封面设计: 王 志

First Edition 2000

Learn to Cook Chinese Dishes
— Cold Dishes

ISBN 7-119-02517-1

Published by Foreign Languages Press
24 Baiwanzhuang Road, Beijing 100037, China
Home Page: http://www.flp.com.cn
E-mail Addresses: info@flp.com.cn
sales@flp.com.cn
Printed in the People's Republic of China

学做中国菜·冷菜类

《学做中国菜》编委会 编

外文出版社出版
(中国北京百万庄大街 24 号)邮政编码 100037
外文出版社网页: http://www.flp.com.cn
外文出版社电子邮件地址: info@flp.com.cn
sales@flp.com.cn
北京骏马行图文中心制版
天时印刷(深圳)有限公司印制
2000 年(24 开)第一版
2000 年第一版第一次印刷
(英汉)
ISBN 7-119-02517-1/J·1522(外)
08000(精)